Princess Island
LEGENDS

by Kanoe Zantua

photography: Tedi Brown

About the Author

Kanoe Zantua has had the desire to write since he was a child. Being a true Alaskan, he loves the wild, mystical beauty of the far north. From his family he has learned the legends of long ago. Kanoe lives on Princess Island — a small, private island found off the coast of Ketchikan, Alaska.

Acknowledgements

Irene Hopkins is Kanoe Zantua's grandmother. He has heard many a tale of Alaska told by her.

Pete Moore is Kanoe's older brother. He is now 25, but at the tender young age of 11 he wrote "Wolves Coming For Me."

First printing
Published by Angelo's Printing & Graphics,
Ketchikan, Alaska, United States of America
Library of Congress

This book is dedicated to:

Mom & Dad
Ken Egerton, my good friend

Raven House

Totem Bight State Park, Ketchikan, Alaska

Contents

Contents cont.

Nature in Alaska

The stream flows reflecting crystal light.
A doe lies nearby with her fawn.
An immature eagle learns to take flight
and the squirrels realize winter is gone.
A seal barks at a dog on the beach.
The canine seems to be intrigued by the sound.
Deep in the forest, the she-bear must teach her cubs to
eat the skunk cabbage that has risen from the ground.
In the blue-green ocean, the Orca searches for food.
And the King salmon leave in fright.
Soon the sun goes and leaves the land in an eerie mood.
As the wolves begin to sing under the Northern Lights.

Fogwoman

It had been weeks since our village ran short of food.
People began to worry, in our bodies, hunger would intrude.
We sent out our hunters to look for deer and bear,
but they came back with nothing, there was nothing there.
Then we went out in our canoes to search for fish,
catching just one or two was our only wish.
We fished for days and then a week, each day turned up empty.
We became so hungry we could barely speak.
So it was back to the village with empty hand.
Our people did not complain, they said they could understand.
It was then I decided I would go out alone.
I felt it was needed, though my people did not condone.
So there I went, back out to sea,
saying I would not return, until I had fish with me.
Again I fished for hours, then days.
My mind and body grew weak, I fell asleep amoung the waves.
When I awoke I was in the middle of a mysterious haze of grey,
an immense fog.
I paddled towards home, at least I thought it was the way.
Time flew by and still no land.
I felt a longing for my people, a need to hold the sand.
Then from the mist an image of a person seemed to appear,
it was very strange.
I could feel inside a growing fear, it grew more as the
apparition moved near.
I could see it now, could see the face
a beautiful body that disappeared without a trace.
I squinted my eyes, trying to see but there was nothing there,
 just me and the sea.
"Hello", a voice said from behind, startled, I turned and saw
an elegant woman whose beauty could make you blind.
I was in awe and could not speak
her hair, body and eyes were dark and sleek.
"You are Raven" she said. How could she know,
I thought through the churning in my head.
"Who are you and where did you come from?"
She quieted me by, on my mouth, placing her thumb.
Again I fell into sleep, awakening sometime later to a shuffle or a quiet creep.
There she was, the woman I had seen before.
She was standing, the sun giving her a silhouette by the door.
Then I realized that I was home.

Fogwoman

She told me she found me where no man had yet to roam.
And I had brought back many things from where I had fished.
She offered herself to me for the things I had accomplished.
My people found a giant yellow cedar log on which they
carved the story of how she saved me from the fog.
Fogwoman she was and married we would be,
until one day I followed her to the sea.
She twirled her fingers in the water of green and blue
and out jumped salmon, two by two.
A woman of beauty and magic as well.
But how she did this she would not tell.
So I secretly followed her there everyday.
After a month I asked again, but she would not say.
"Then you must leave," I said pointing to the sea
once again she vanished right before me.
And once more the fog, was all I could see
as it rolled away I heard her call to me
I will return salmon to your streams every year,
but you will never see me again
my love, my dear.

Eagle Boy

During the warm summer nights, the chief's nephew would go down the narrow piece of land that stuck out into the ocean. The boy would go out on the land by the ocean to feed the eagles.

The other villagers began to call him Eagle Boy. They didn't like it when he went to watch the eagles as they flew high in the sky. The villagers did not understand what Eagle Boy saw in the mighty birds. "You are lazy," one of the men told Eagle Boy.

"Why do you say that?" the boy asked innocently.

"You sit on the beach in the sun watching the eagles while the people of your village dry food for the winter. You also feed the eagles too often. They are birds and can feed themselves," the man said.

"But they are hungry," the boy protested.

Eagle Boy's grandmother watched him from the clan house. She strongly believed, in her heart, that Eagle Boy would prove himself to the village one day.

As the months went by, the days began to get colder and darker. Soon the village was out of food. The chief decided to move everyone to a place in the north. Everyone except for Eagle Boy.

"You cannot go," he declared.

"But I will starve," the boy said.

"Maybe you should have helped your village during the summer. Maybe then you would not have to stay behind," the chief said.

Without further words, the chief and the other villagers climbed into their canoes and left for the rivers to

Eagle Boy

the north. Eagle Boy stood on the rocks and waved to his grandmother. She did not want to leave him, but she could not bring him and she could not stay. Tears began to stream down the cheeks of the grandmother's face as she waved goodbye to her grandson.

For the next couple of nights, Eagle Boy sat by a small fire that he had built. He was lonely and hungry. He watched with eyes of hope as an eagle flew near him. Eagle Boy could see that the eagle was holding a salmon in its talons. It swooped down near the boy and dropped the salmon. Eagle Boy stumbled on the rocks as he ran to get the food. He smiled and then laughed with joy as more eagles came with food for him. They were repaying him for feeding them when they did not have food.

In the north, Eagle Boy's uncle was not doing well in finding food for his people. The rivers did not have any salmon in them and the people were starving. They decided to go back to their old village.

When the villagers arrived at the beach, they noticed all the food that Eagle Boy had. They saw how strong and healthy he was and could not believe their eyes.

"Where did you get all this food?" his uncle asked.

"The eagles gave it to me. They were saying thank you for feeding them when they needed it," Eagle Boy said. "Sometimes it pays to help someone or something that is in need," he continued as he held some food out to his uncle. "I have plenty for everyone," he said.

His people were so happy to have food, they gave Eagle Boy many furs and pieces of jewelry. He became a well respected young man in the village and it made Eagle Boy's grandmother cry once again. This time she cried tears of happiness.

The Legend of Mankind

The world was dark inside where the humans lived. They kept themselves secret until one day a great bird would come to find them.

And so it went ... Raven, who ruled the world, came upon a huge clam shell sticking out of the mud flats. He flew down, walked around it a few times, noticing a small crack. Raven cocked his head to one side. His eye peering closer to the opening. He could hear unfamiliar voices coming from within the clam shell.

Once again, Raven's curiosity gets the best of him. He thrusts his beak into the clam shell with such force that the shell pops open. Startled, he steps back as mankind emerges from the shell. Astonished as Raven, the humans gasp at the sight of this mighty bird and the world around them. Raven knows that he has opened the door to his destiny.

The Sun and Raven

Long ago, the chief of the Nass River held the sun captive inside a bent wood box inside his tribal house. Outside the world was dark and cold. Many of the young villagers had never seen sunlight.

One day, a brave white bird named Raven decided he would somehow get into the chief's tribal house and release the sun. It was not going to be an easy job. Raven knew he could not just fly through the clan house door because the chief did not like him and did not trust him either.

Raven was known to be able to change his shape. He could change into something as small as an ant or something as large as a tree. Many people believed that Raven could turn into a small insect to get inside the tribal house. This was not true. The chief had put a spell on his house that would only allow humans inside.

For a while Raven was worried that the world would remain dark and cold forever, but after many days of thought, he had a plan to get inside the clan house. He knew that every morning the chief's daughter would walk to the river and get water for her family. She always dipped her wooden spoon in the water and took a small sip.

Early one morning, Raven followed the chief's daughter to the river. He flew a few feet upstream from her and turned into a hemlock needle. The needle fell into the river and floated towards the young woman. She sat next to the river and scooped some water with her bucket. She then dipped her spoon in the bucket and brought the fresh water to her lips. Slowly the chief's daughter drank the spoonful of water. She did not know that she had also swallowed the hemlock needle.

The Sun and Raven

Nine months went by and the chief's daughter gave birth to a healthy baby boy. She did not know how she became pregnant, but she did not care. The young woman loved her baby and her father did too. No one in the village knew that the baby was Raven. As the years went by, the boy's grandfather became very close to him. The chief loved his grandson more than almost anything. As soon as the boy was able to talk, he asked his grandfather if he could play with the bent wood box that contained the sun. The chief frowned and said no. He told the boy he was allowed to play with anything except the bent wood box. The boy began to cry and cry. He cried for days and would not eat.

Soon the boy's mother began to worry about her son and begged her father to let the boy play with the bent wood box. The chief remained stern at first, but finally gave in because he could no longer bear to see his family in pain. The chief handed the box to his grandson and said he could play with it. He told the boy not to open it because if he did, the boy would be punished. The young child said he would obey his grandfather. Pleased with the boy's reply, the chief left the tribal house.

As soon as the chief was gone, the boy began to transform back into Raven. He lifted the lid of the box and the sun slowly rose upwards. The chief saw the light coming through the door and ran inside his house. To his amazement and displeasure, he saw the sun and Raven. The chief quickly ordered the guards to close the door to the tribal house.

The sun was still rising and was almost through the smoke hole. Raven flew around and around waiting for the sun to go through the hole, but to his surprise, it stopped. The sun was stuck in the smoke hole. Raven flew to the sun and pushed with all his might. His wings flapping harder than they had ever flapped. The sun would not budge at first, but after much

The Sun and Raven

effort it gave in and moved through the smoke hole. As it moved through, some of the sun's rays broke off and sailed into the sky. The rays became the moon and the stars.

Raven knew the only way out was through the smoke hole, so up he went. He brushed against a side of the wall and the coal from the smoke hole covered Raven's body until he was completely black. When the villagers around the world saw the sun, the moon, and the stars, they became to scream with joy. The world was once again light and warm. Raven was a hero and his amazing story was passed on through the generations.

Whale's World

It was one of the worst winters ever. The wind howled throughout the day and the ocean's waves often rose ten feet high. Snow fell for days until the land was all white. Fishermen tried, but they could not stay out in the rough water long enough to catch fish. The snow was so thick that hunters could not travel very far to find food for their people.

At dawn each day, the chief's daughter would drape her yellow cedar blanket upon her shoulders to keep the chill of winter off as she walked to the high rocks that overlooked the fishing grounds. Day after day she would go there to see if the white caps had ceased, but the water was always rough. The waves crashed hard against the beach as if they were trying to wash it all away.

One morning, Killer Whale appeared before the chief's daughter. She explained to him that the waves were too powerful and her people could not fish from the ocean. Killer Whale understood and he said, "If you come with me, I will make sure your village always has food throughout the seasons." The chief's daughter thought about it for a few moments then agreed to go and be with him.

Killer Whale was so happy that he chased the sea lions ashore and the salmon to the streams.

The daughter kept her promise and climbed upon Killer Whale's back where she would always be with him.

The villagers still give thanks as they watch the chief's daughter, who has become the dorsal fin of the Killer Whale, riding by the high rocks.

Killer Whale

I saw it shoot through the water two-colored and huge.
I wanted to run for shelter, some kind of refuge.
It burst out of the water giving me warning.
That if I moved nearer its calf my mother would be in mourning.
I stood there in my rickety boat,
thanking the stars I was still afloat.
It zoomed by again as if in anger.
I knew he didn't like me for I was a stranger.
As it swam away, its fin like a sail,
I knew right then, my eyes did not fail,
I had seen a bull killer whale.

The Orca and the Swans

The young orca swam through the blue-green ocean with his pod. Swimming steadily behind his mother, father and sisters, he had thoughts of rebellion. The orca was tired of always being with his family and wanted to go off on his own. He dreamed of chasing schools of king salmon and baby seals. He wanted to be known as the most ferocious of all orca whales.

A few days later when his family was hunting for salmon, Orca decided he would swim away when he wasn't being watched. A school of sockeye swam by and the pod of whales immediately gave chase. While his parents and sisters chased the fish, the young orca swam away from them to capture his dreams.

For one year, the orca terrorized the seas, eating many salmon and seals. He ate so many salmon that the human fishermen soon grew tired of him. They decided to catch him before he ate all the salmon in the ocean.

The orca shot through the water after yet another school of salmon. His jaws wide open, showing red stained teeth. When he was almost to the salmon, wide nets fell before him. The

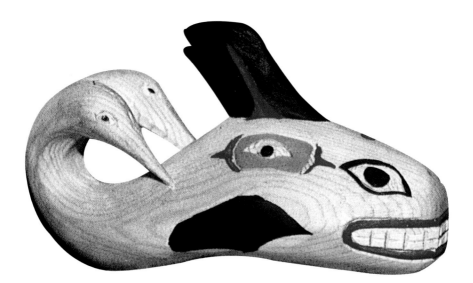

The Orca and the Swans

orca jerked to the right, but there was a net there too. Frightened, he turned to flee, but it was too late. The nets surrounded him and pulled him towards the water's surface. He looked around with horrified eyes at the fishermen. One of them walked up to him with a big ax and said, "You are a greedy whale and have eaten most of the fish in this area. Because of you, some of the villages might go hungry this winter. But you will do no more harm to anyone. Without a tail, you cannot swim and won't be able to chase the fish that we live off of."

The ax dropped down and the orca's fluke fell into the water. The nets released him. He cried as he fell into the sea. He flipped his fins rapidly, but did not move. Then a thought of terror ran through his mind. He knew he would drown if he did not find a way back to the surface within the next few minutes. Again, the young orca moved his powerful fins attempting to rise through the water. A surge of joy ran through his black and white body as he moved upwards very slowly. After a few minutes of painful fin thrusts, the orca made it to the surface. A rush of breath flew out of his blow-hole spraying water about five feet in the air. He stopped waving his fins and was happy to see that he could float on the surface without the help of his fins. He began to cry again, wishing he had never left his family. Now he realized how much he loved them and how much he needed them. Throughout the night and into the morning, tears flowed through his eyes.

Towards the afternoon, two elegant swans swam to him. They had heard his cries of sorrow and wondered what could have saddened such a huge mammal.

"Why are you crying?" one of the swans asked.

"I left my family to become the most famous whale of all, but my greed became too much making some fishermen cut off my fluke."

"How were you being greedy?" the swans asked.

"I tried to eat all the fish and seals in the sea," he replied, "and now I just want to find my family again and be happy."

The Orca and the Swans

The swans swam away to where the young orca could not hear them. They talked to each other for awhile and then went back to the whale. "We will help you find your family if you promise not to ever eat more fish or seals than you need."

"But, how will I follow you?" the orca asked. "I don't have my fluke."

"Do not ask questions. Just yes or no, will you stop being greedy if we help you?" the male swan said.

The orca was not sure about this, but he replied, "yes."

The two swans swam to the rear of the orca and began to change shape. Before the orca realized what was happening, the swans were gone. Then to the orca's surprise, he could sense that his fluke was back. He joyfully swished it back and forth then dove down through the water in search of his family.

After a few days of travel, the young orca reunited with his family. He apologized for leaving them and kept his promise to the swans who had joined with him to become his new fluke. He never again ate more than he needed. He had learned his lesson about greed.

Eagle's Human Legacy

I hear him grandfather. His call is echoing off the hills. It
sounds so important.

He is calling to you my son.
To look into the future as he has done.
For it is Eagle who has the most powerful vision.
It is he who represents fame and power.
Eagle has always protected this village from harm.

You are in the
Eagle Clan my son.
Follow in Eagle's direction.
Become strong
like his wings
and powerful
like his call.

Eagle will always
guide you.

Grandfather,
you know Eagle
so well.

Yes my son, for
I am he.

Halibut Stew

Frog told this story and he told it true.
How Raven with Eagle made Halibut Stew.
Frog led the trio to the shore of the ocean.
Where he told of a great fish, who made quite a commotion.
Eagle and Raven decided to trick him along,
so they sent frog to the shore to sing a great song.
Halibut, the fish, followed the tune
that led him to a narrow gape by noon.
The trio, so clever, swam, hopped and flew,
until Eagle and Raven got their Halibut Stew.

Eagle with Chilkat Blanket

Master Carpenter Totem

Wolves

I hear them once a winter's day.
Hear them hunting, searching for their prey.

They're quick and silent when making their kill.
They only take what they need to have their fill.

People say their songs are a little bit eerie,
that they kill man I think is a theory.

I can see them in stores made of rock molded.
But, I'd rather see them real, their eyes glowing golden.

I hear them all through Alaska's mountains and coves.
I hear their songs. The songs of wolves.

The Wolf

by Irene Hopkins

Oh, wolf, I felt your presence flicker by,
before your shadow caught my eye,
emerging from some lonesome glade,
half hidden by the forest shade.

I saw your yellow gleaming eyes,
a look so cold and yet so wise!
Stiff hairs rising along your back,
victorious ruler of the pack.

You wild and savage, sleek of line,
why seek you man from time to time?

Is it some ancient, vagrant urging,
for his companionship, emerging,
or have you brought wolf pack around
to howl that eerie, longing, lonesome sound?

Wolves Coming For Me

by Pete Moore

I heard the wolves
howling.

I heard the wolves
tracking.

I heard the wolves
killing.

I heard the wolves
devouring.

I heard the wolves come for me.

Bear's Tummy Ache

Eagle flying high could not believe what he saw.
Bear had yet another salmon in his paw.
If Eagle had a human face as he soared down.
Then across it you would find a mighty large frown.
Don't you think you're being just a little bit greedy?
He said to Bear his eyes small and beady.
Be gone! Bear said with a very loud roar.
And so he did. Eagle did soar.
So eat them all, I don't care.
Just see how well your tummy will fare.
Later that day Eagle flew back with crow.
They found Bear asleep next to the river's flow.
His tummy was big. No, a better word's huge.
Eagle laughed, you could tell he was amused.
You ate all the salmon you sleeping fool.
Now as you lie there with your tummy ache
you'll sleep all winter in a hibernate state.
Now, I can eat all I want
and laugh and tease, fly and taunt.
This is more than any eagle could ever want.

Seawoman

Seawoman looked towards the sea as she wept.
She was afraid that death had completed
    the vows she had kept.
Weeks had passed since her husband had gone.
He told Seawoman he would return the next dawn.
She waited and waited, standing still by the shore.
As each day departed, sorrow tore at her heart's core.
Seawoman asked the wise owl to look.
When owl returned he said, "I'm sorry
    I could not find the path your husband took.
She became desperate and asked the orca whale.
But, he too came back with nothing. He too had failed.
As Seawoman looked out towards the sea,
Raven swooped down with news to answer her plea.
You have found my husband. Please tell me its true.
Raven said yes, now let me tell you.
In a vision, I saw your love on a faraway land.
He was taken there by Mother Nature's hand.
My vision said he will return in one season.
That is why he has taken so long. That is the reason.
Seawoman's eyes were wide. She never did blink.
When she bent down and kissed Raven's kind beak.

Bear Mother

For days Bear Mother could be heard crashing through the forest in search of her lost cub. She knew that he had the power to change his shape and this worried her. Bear Mother was afraid that if her son had changed shape, she would not be able to recognize him.

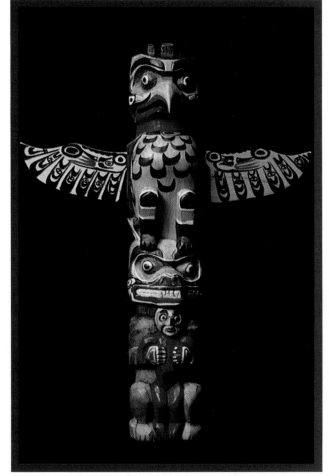

Eagle came to her and told her of a brave new man who was to be trained to be chief of a nearby village. He said she should follow him to the village to watch the upcoming ceremonies.

Bear Mother followed Eagle to the village hoping that this brave new chief could help her find her son.

As they came closer to the village, Bear Mother heard a familiar sound. She moved faster toward the sound until the new chief stood in front of them. Bear Mother recognized the man at once. It was her son.

Eagle

by Irene Hopkins

O, Mighty Eagle, Feathered King,
Greatest of all in spread of wing.
With glistening white of head and tail,
In silence o'er the Forest sail.

Fiercest of all the birds of the air,
Oh, from your screaming dive, beware!
Of keenest eyes, and mighty wings,
Prepare to die, you lesser beings!

Sailing high above the day,
You fiercely spy your scuttling prey.
And as your diving nears, a running creature hears,
Your screaming battlecry, and knows that it will die.

Now spiraling high,
A speck upon the blue,
Your searching eye,
Still keen and true.

So fierce and yet so mild,
To your hungry Eaglet child.
Returning to your spacious nest,
From many a bounteous quest,
To feed that endless hunger —
No time to rest — No time to linger.

Once more to hunt,
Return to feed,
That always cavernous
Mouth in need.

Eagle

Still to teach your young to fly,
And them the heights to occupy.
At last to rest the Winter thru,
And sail again into the blue.

Majestic hunter of the sky,
Causing all below to fear,
Stalking all Southeast from high,
Is Man your only peer?

A lonely sentinel o'er the sea?
Perched high in mighty cedar tree?
Long may you fly so free,
You are a thrill to me!

Eagle

With a dark brown body and white feathered head,
the beautiful raptures fly, through the cloud scattered sky.
Gathering herring to feed their young that lie screeching in
a nest shaped bed.
They sit by river beds, feasting on salmon that have died.
And soar over meadows where wolves have cried.
Glorified, turned into a symbol of a mighty nation,
they are pictured on forms of money and family crests.
Treasured by natives before our country's creation.
All this, and protected by law, they couldn't ask for less.
Their stories passed down the generations by the old.
They are clever,
majestic and
bold.

The Coming

The young chief stood watching the last of the snow glisten off the treetops. Mist rose throughout the forest into the clear morning sky.

There was a sound like something breaking that the chief could hear off in the distance. He decided to go see what had caused the noise. The chief ran towards the sound which had come from the ocean. As he moved quickly for the water, he could hear ice crushing against itself.

Something was in the air. He didn't know what it was, but it felt wonderful! The chief knew that what he was hearing was going to turn out to be something very nice. He ran now with great energy towards the ocean. As he came closer, the chief saw an eagle through the trees, the white head and dark feathered body. The young man's excitement soared high as he heard the screech of another eagle nearby.

When the chief reached the ocean, he saw nothing of interest. He turned back towards the forest in disappointment. As he was about to go into the woods, he heard the sound of something breathing behind him. The chief stopped to listen for the sound again. There was silence, then he heard it again. The man whirled around and saw the back of a giant animal in the ocean. Water sprayed from the mammal's back as it moved further toward the north. The animal did something that the chief had seen before at that time of year. The whale dove down into the water and then shot up towards the surface. The water's surface broke as one of the Orca lunged upward. The whale's body turned slightly to the right as it fell back into the water. Soon the other whales began to do the same thing, though not very often.

After watching the whales for a few minutes, the chief shouted with happiness into the air. He then ran full speed back to his village calling, "They are here! They are here! The Orca are here." The chief stopped to catch his breath, then he shouted to the village with excitement, "It is the beginning of Spring!"

The Legend of Thunderbird

A young boy stood by the ocean's shore watching a small pod of Sperm whales playing in the bay. They dove, breeched and sometimes gave chase to schools of small fish.

There was a rumbling sound far off behind the mountains. The boy listened carefully, trying to figure out what the noise was. It came steadily closer and closer. Now the sound was more like a thunder clap than rumbling. Trying to ignore the thunder, he began to watch the whales again.

A massive shadow spread across the water falling next to the boy. At first, he thought the shadow was from a cloud, but he changed his mind when he heard a horrendously loud screech from the sky. Looking up, he saw a giant bird swooping towards the ocean. The bird's eyes flashed like lightening bolts. The flapping of its wings sounded like thunder. The giant bird's talons stretched out, its claws wide open. With a huge splash like geyser spray, the bird hit the water. The boy let out a terrorizing scream when he saw what was in the bird's talons. The bird, paying no attention to him, slowly rose from the water. Its powerful wings struggled to hold onto its prey. Water flowed from the Sperm whale as it struggled to free itself from the tight grip of the talons. The whale moved helplessly, like a young fish caught in the pincers of a crab. Higher and higher the bird flew until it was further up than the trees. It flew up above the mountains before it let out an ear-shattering screech. The whale was too heavy, forcing the bird to fall from the sky. Without a choice, the giant bird reluctantly dropped the whale on top of one of the mountains.

Upon returning to the village the boy told his story to his grandfather who was honored to tell his grandson that he too, in his youth, had seen the Mighty Thunderbird.

Blackskin

Blackskin, Blackskin
How strong you must be
To tear the Sea Lion apart
For all to see.

So many nights by the fire you kept,
Your desire so strong, you hardly slept.
Each icy dip into the ocean at night
While the village was quiet, without light.

You fought the North wind again and again
Until it finally gave in — for you a win!

We know it took you so long
to gain the strength to fight.
You needed will, courage and might.
For that eventful day out in the sea,
Your reward — a leader of the village to be.

Spirit of the Raven

by Irene Hopkins

O Raven, bird of ancient days,
Clever bird of wiley ways,
Mighty king of all Southeast
Ruler of each bird and beast.

As each day of dawning's near,
I hear your eerie callings clear.
O Raven, calling from the heights
Where do you spend your nights?

Atop some mighty cedar tree,
Overlooking stormy sea?
Or on some spiraling cliff top home,
Where but the wild goat dares to roam?

O bird of humor, not of prey,
Perching high above the day,
Exulting in the early dawn,
Who is your joke upon?

O laughing at your latest feat,
Outwitting all you chance to meet?
From watching you I know,
Your bravado's not for show,

Nor is your nature but to clown —
I've seen you face the Eagle down,
And send him winging for the skies,
While you, the victor, scorn the prize.

Spirit of the Raven

O, Raven, do you remember when
All Southeast was fog and sea?
I was your Brother, then.
Do you remember me?

O, Raven, sailor of the air,
O bird who never has a care,
In my dreams at night we ride,
On air currents, side by side.

O, Raven flying o'er the sea —
Conquerer of all the sky,
While from earth I long to be
Your companion, by and by.

Light-winged King of all that you survey,
We salute you on your way.

Princess Raven

Princess Raven, daughter of the chief of the Nass River, who at one time held the sun captive, was a very beautiful and powerful young lady. She was loved by all the people in her village because she was kind and giving, unlike her father.

Raven had watched the princess from the treetops since her birth. As she became older, Raven was breathless at the sight of her beauty. He fell in love with her, but did not think he could gain her love because her father did not trust him. The chief called Raven a trickster and had his guards watch the sky and trees for Raven's presence.

One day Raven built up enough courage to go talk to the princess. He waited until she went to her favorite stream to collect water. When she arrived, Raven flew down and landed next to her. The princess looked at him, her brown eyes sparkling in the sunlight. Her dark brown hair moved with the soft spring air. She smiled, her teeth gleaming white. "Beautiful princess, I have watched you from above since the day you were born. I feel a great love for you and would like to be with you forever."

"I have seen you watching me before. I think you are very kind, but my father would never allow me to marry you," the princess explained.

"Then can we spend the day together?" Raven asked.

Princess nodded and sat down on the grass by the river. Throughout the day, Raven told the princess stories and made her laugh. She really liked Raven and began thinking about her father. Finally, she said, "I do not care what my father thinks. I want to always be with you, but how do we keep my father out of this?"

Princess Raven

The chief did not like Raven because he could transform himself into various things. He thought about turning himself into a human, but Raven wanted the chief to be able to notice his presence when he saw the princess. "I will fly into the air above the river and turn myself into a hemlock needle. When it floats down to you, pick it up and swallow it."

Princess nodded and wondered what was going to happen as Raven flew into the air. In an instant he was gone. A small hemlock needle slowly fell towards the water. When it floated down to her, princess picked it up and swallowed it. She waited, but nothing happened. Then she felt a jerk in her back. The princess reached back to see what the pain was and to her surprise, she felt feathers. A wing grew out of her back and wrapped around her. It was so warm. The princess felt a love like never before.

Raven and the princess were joined together throughout all time. All creatures that saw them could feel the love drifting from the face of the princess and the wing of Raven.

The Lady By The Sea

Blue eyes sparkle like sun lite sea.

Light honey blonde hair more beautiful than most wish to be.

She is short like people from olden day lore.

But stands tall and elegant by the ocean's shore.

She watches the schools of salmon chase the herring by.

And gazes at the majestic eagle soaring through the sky.

Sometimes you can see her standing by the shore at night,

if the waves allow and the moonlight's right.

She is the one whom with I long to be.

Her standing there. The lady by the sea.